HERE
and THERE
with the BIBLE

Illustrated by HERTHA DEPPER

HERE
and THERE
with the BIBLE

by Elizabeth Allstrom

FRIENDSHIP PRESS   NEW YORK

Contents

For my sister

1

The Fourth Train Stop

Whoo-whoo-whoo-oooo.

It was late one summer afternoon when the distant train whistle sounded faintly through the village of Nigeria where Uday lived. Uday, playing alone on his porch, looked up from the snail shell that he was spinning along the floor like a dancing top.

Then, as the whistle sounded again—whoo-whoo-whoo-oooo—he jumped to his feet in excitement. "Father's bringing special news today! I can tell!" he said to himself. And again he wished, as he often did, that he could know the news when it happened.

Uday was proud that Father was a railroad engineer, an important man in their African town. He was proud of the family's neatly painted house that the railroad company had built for them. He was proud of Father's engine that went puffing out from town every morning. It pulled two small cars and carried people and freight to the end of the line. It made seven stops on the way and then came back home in the afternoon.

Uday liked to think that every morning, when the whistle sounded as the train left the station, Father was sending a message to him, "Leav-ing-now, leav-ing-now." And that every afternoon when the train headed for home to rest for the night, the whistle called to him again, "Soon-be-there, soon-be-there."

On some of the days when Uday heard the whistle, he was certain that Father was announcing special news. The whistle had called in a special way the time Father had news about the fire he had seen in the town at the end of the line. And again when thir-teen cows had been grazing on the grass between the tracks and Father and the fireman had had to climb down and chase them away so the train could con-tinue on its way. And especially the time Father had brought news of his present from the railroad company for good service—a gold watch and chain that he now wore every day.

Today the whistle was sounding in the special way. Uday looked off in the direction of the home-coming train. "Some day when I'm nine or maybe ten I'll ride on the engine with Father. He promised! Then I'll know the news when it happens."

But this was no time to think about such far-off days! Since morning Uday had been spinning his new snail shell, first at his friend Chuku's house, then on his own porch. Now Father was almost home, and not one of Uday's daily chores was done.

Stuffing the snail shell into his pocket for safe-keeping, Uday dashed into the house, muttering at himself all the way for having put off doing the chores. Now he must hurry.

Back in a moment with a large basket, he quickly picked up the ripe mangoes and oranges that had fallen into the yard during the day, piled them high in the basket, and carried them into the kitchen, glad that none toppled off to be picked up again.

Then, grabbing up the bucket, he took it to the pipe to draw the water that Mother needed for cooking. Next he went to the field where the family's sheep had been grazing since early morning and brought them back to the yard for the night. Then, noticing with annoyance that Grandmother's fine red rooster was out of his pen, Uday stopped to shoo him back inside to be safe for the night. This rooster was a valuable creature, and all the family had to help keep him safe. Father had bought him at the government farm, and he was worth more than all the other chickens put together.

The work finished at last, Uday called to Mother and Grandmother in the kitchen, "I'll go now and meet Father." But his words really meant, "I'll go now and be the first to hear Father's news."

Nearing the station, Uday saw that Father had already climbed down from his engine and the trackmen had backed the engine around to be ready for its trip next day. Uday waved, and Father called his usual greeting. But Father told no special news.

On the way home, Uday carried Father's lunchbox and empty water flask. Still Father talked only about the usual happenings. "Is your new snail shell a good spinner?—Are the sheep in the yard for the night?—Did Grandmother's rooster get out again?"

Even while resting in his chair on the porch and waiting for supper, Father mentioned nothing special. Later, as the family ate the evening meal, Uday hoped Father would speak out, but he didn't.

"I guess when Father's ready, then he'll tell his news," Uday thought. Perhaps the whistle today had been no different than on ordinary days.

After supper, when darkness fell, Father as usual lighted the hurricane lamp on the table. Uday, Mother, and Grandmother sat quietly while he opened the Bible and read aloud the Shepherd's Psalm. This was Uday's favorite.

> The Lord, like a shepherd, cares for me.
> It is he who looks after me, as a man looks
> after his sheep and his goats. . . .

Uday had heard the familiar verses more times than he could count. He could read the words for himself, and he knew almost all of them from memory. God's love and care were not hard for him to understand. They were something like Father's love for him, only better. They were something like his own care for the family's sheep and for Grandmother's red rooster, only better.

After the evening worship, Father held up the Bible in his hands and made an announcement. "Tomorrow when I go on the train I will carry this with me. When the engine takes on water at the Fourth Train Stop, my fireman's wife and small daughter will come to the station for their first Bible lesson. He wants them to see the Bible and to hear the same stories I have told to him."

Father's news at last! Uday wiggled in excitement. Father taking the Bible on the train! Father being like a preacher! Why, this was better news than the fire or the cows or even the gold watch and chain. And tomorrow night there would be more of it, when Father told all that happened at the Fourth Stop.

Now Father looked at his watch and turned out the lamp. Time for bed! But Uday was not ready for sleep for a long time. Wishing thoughts kept spinning around in his head as fast as his snail shell had been spinning around on the porch.

The next morning when Uday wakened, the sun was already up. Fragrant smells told him that Mother was serving the bean porridge and fish, that Grandmother was preparing Father's lunch. Bleating sounds told him that the sheep were growing impatient, eager to be taken to the grazing place.

Uday ate his breakfast and finished the morning chores. When he returned to the yard, he saw that Father had not yet left for the station. Instead, he was dashing across the yard, first in one direction, then in another. His shouts warned of the trouble. "Grandmother's red rooster is out of the pen again. There he is, over by the gate—no—by the porch. If we don't get this valuable creature back where he belongs, he'll certainly end up in some family's supper pot!"

Uday joined the wild and noisy chase. Finally he and Father were so tired and out of breath that they were ready to give up in despair, when the little rooster, his head held high, strutted back into the pen as though he had caused no trouble at all.

Father reached up to fasten the bolt on the pen door. "No wonder this fellow gets out so easily!" he exclaimed. "Why didn't you tell me the bolt was loose? But I cannot stop to fix it now. I am already late. This, I think, will hold it until night." And Father forced a small twig into the bolt, making it firm. "Come, walk with me to the station. We'll talk about some other jobs that you and I must do together."

Talking while they walked, they had almost reached the station when Father suddenly stopped and slapped the pockets of his jacket. "My Bible! I've come off without it, and I must take it with me. Run home and bring it to me. If you hurry, I think there'll be time while the engine gets up steam."

Uday raced for home. A falling mango struck the path beside him. His bare feet stumbled over a stone. Chuku called from his yard.

Uday did not stop. His only thought was to reach home, scoop up the Bible, and get it to Father before the train pulled away.

At home Uday looked on the table by the hurricane lamp. The Bible was not there. He looked beside Father's chair on the porch. It was not there. It was not in the kitchen. Uday remembered that Father read from the Bible as soon as he wakened every morning, so he looked by Father's bed, but the book was not there.

When Uday asked Mother, she said, "Father had it right after breakfast. Look on the step by the back door." Sure enough, there it was!

Hugging the precious book, Uday started back, running full speed toward the station. A barking dog chased at his heels. A neighbor waved to him. Chuku called to him again. But Uday hurried on. When he caught sight of the train, it was beginning to move slowly away from the station, away from the stationmaster standing in his place on the platform. The whistle called, "Leav-ing-now, leaving-now."

Uday ran along beside the moving engine. "Father, the Bible!" he called.

Father's words flashed down to him from above. "Hold it tight! Stretch your arm up!"

Uday did as Father said, and in another moment he felt himself swept off the ground and swung up into the cab of the puffing engine. He heard Father's words called back to the stationmaster, "Please tell Mother that Uday is with me for the day."

As the train traveled on toward the Fourth Stop, Uday thought about his good fortune at not having to wait until he was nine or maybe ten to be riding in the jiggity-jiggy engine with Father. He was riding there now!

But he also had other thoughts—how cool the breeze would feel on his arm if he poked it out the window. He was about to try it when Father said, "Arms and hands belong inside." —How shrill the whistle would sound if he gave the string a little pull. He was about to try it when Father said, "The trainmen give the signals on this train." —How easy it would be to put coal on the fire. He was about to reach for the shovel when Father said, "The fireman tends fires on this train."

So Uday had to be content with just watching all that was flying past outside.

At the Fourth Stop, Father drew the engine up beside the water tank. While the pump men filled the boiler, Uday and Father followed the fireman to a shady place nearby where the fireman's wife and daughter waited on their mats.

Father showed them the Bible, then read them a story from it. They were pleased and asked for one more, but already the whistle was signaling, "Time-to-go, time-to-go." Father looked at his watch. "Another day you shall have another lesson," he promised his new pupils. "Now we must take our passengers and freight on to their places on time."

Uday was ready to say good-by also when suddenly he felt Father's Bible being put into his hands and heard Father's whisper. "You stay and give them another lesson. You can tell the stories and read the verses. When I come back, I'll pick you up."

Uday took the Bible and turned the pages to the verses about the shepherd. He slowly spoke the familiar words:

> The Lord, like a shepherd, cares for me.
> It is he who looks after me. . . .

The mother and little girl repeated the words after him. Soon they, too, knew them from memory.

Uday shared other parts of the Bible that he knew, and all the while he was wiggling in excitement.

He had traveled on the train with Father and the Bible!

He had been like a preacher!

He was knowing the news when it happened!

Why, today he was the person making the news!

New Words in the Story

Chuku   CHOO-koo   Uday   oo-day

2

The Piece of Good Luck

Seven-year-old Gopal was tired. Father and Mother were tired. They had walked for many miles over dusty roads from their village in India to the town where the festival was to be held. And they were hungry. It had been many hours since Gopal and his parents had eaten their early morning bowl of rice.

Now as they entered the town, they joined the crowds of other travelers. Everyone had come for the great celebration in honor of the god whose statue, carved in stone, stood in the temple. During the celebration everyone would visit the temple and leave gifts there for the god.

As Gopal, Father, and Mother walked along, Father pointed to the many visitors. "Look," he said in a worried tone. "You can see for yourselves that except for us every person has a gift for the god.

What Father said was true. But Mother reminded him, "After all, it isn't our fault that we have no gifts. We started out with them—the fruit and grain and precious cooking butter. We meant to bring them. Then our bad luck came."

Gopal said, "If we tell the god of the temple about the bad luck, maybe he won't be angry with us."

Father and Mother did not answer, and Gopal knew why. Was not the temple god already angry with the family? Had he not allowed the bad luck to fall upon them from the moment they left their home? Had he not let their troubles pile up one on top of another for the whole journey?

In silence Gopal, Father, and Mother moved slowly along with the visitors toward the temple. At least they could go inside. At least they could spread their sleeping mats in the temple yard.

Now they moved past the small cooking fires

where some of the travelers were preparing their food. Now they passed old men sitting cross-legged beside their bowls, begging coins from the passers-by. On they went, past the musicians playing their flutes and drums, past merchants calling out their wares from gaily decorated booths.

Jalebis! Sweets!
I have good sweets!
Come and buy!

Chai! Garum chai!
Tea! Hot tea!

Gopal wished for one of the syrupy sweets for himself. He knew that Father and Mother would like hot tea. But Father could spare no money for these treats, not even one small coin for a beggar's bowl. His coins were needed to buy fuel for the cooking fire and food for eating during the festival.

Coming at last to the temple yard, Father said, "Here near the temple we'll unroll our mats and put up the cooking pot. Here we'll stay for the days of the celebration."

In the yard the gatekeeper noticed the family's sleeping mats, their cooking pot, their small bag of rice. His quick eyes noticed, too, that the family carried no gifts. "Where are your gifts for the god of the temple?" he demanded angrily.

Father shook his head. Mother said nothing. But Gopal spoke right out. "Sir—the bad luck—we—"

The gatekeeper waited to hear no more. He shook his arm at them. "Move on," he directed in a rough voice, motioning them away. "There's no room here for you. Go find another place."

More bad luck! Was this then their welcome to the festival—angry words shouted at them—no place to stay—no friend to understand their troubles?

Father led them hastily outside the temple yard. There, a little beyond the high sloping grassy bank, Gopal, Father, and Mother came to a shady grove of trees. "This will be our place," Father said.

They all were glad. Soon they could eat and rest. Mother unrolled the mats. Father put the cooking pot in place, then went to buy fuel and food. Soon they were seated, eating their simple meal.

Dust from the roads and smoke from the many fires formed a foglike haze over all the town. Sounds of fun and laughter came from every direction. Gopal wished he could see for himself all that was happening. He pointed to the top of the grassy slope. "I'll go up there and watch for a while."

Father and Mother said, "Very well. We'll rest here near the fire. Don't get lost."

Moments later, perched high on the top of the bank, Gopal looked down and all around him. In all his seven years he had never seen such sights!

Below him on one side of the bank was the sacred pool of water. Here people were bathing to be clean before going into the temple to worship. Beyond the pool was the temple. Visitors with their gifts were going through the wide doorway.

Below him on the other side were the festival entertainers, dressed in bright clothes—blue, purple, red, green. Magicians whirled swords high above their heads. Acrobats turned somersaults through hoops. Dancers held hands and caught laughing children and grownups in their turning circle.

Looking down at the festival crowds, Gopal could still hear in his mind the gatekeeper's angry words because they had had no gifts—"Move on! There's no room here for you. Go find another place."

He thought of the pieces of bad luck that had followed the family all the way from home to the festival town. First, Father's fever had come back, and the family had had to spend two nights beside the road until he got better. Then Mother had turned her ankle, and they had had to walk slowly so she would not feel the pain so much. Then Gopal himself had run off to play with some village boys and had got lost for a while. Mother and Father had had to wait for him.

As a result, the journey had taken longer than planned, and the family had used up their supply of food. In their hunger they had eaten the fruit and grain gifts meant for the temple god. They had given the cooking butter to pay for medicine for Father and a bandage for Mother's ankle. Not one gift was left to give the god in the temple.

"Somewhere down there in the crowds," thought

Gopal, "there must be a piece of good luck. I'll watch for it. When I find it, I'll hold it. I won't let it go."

Suddenly the sound of music came up to Gopal from a place at the edge of the grassy slope. He looked but saw no flute player, no drum player. He saw only a young man standing beside a big box on a table. Could the music be coming out of the box, he wondered. Curious, Gopal left his perch on the high bank and scurried down the grassy slope. He joined other listeners who had quickly gathered around the box.

The music finished, the young man picked up one of the bright pictures spread out on the table beside the box. A voice called, "Story!" Gopal moved nearer to the young man.

Now the young man held the paper high so that from all sides the people could see the woman on the donkey and the kind man pictured beside her. Then he began to tell the story about them. "Mary and Joseph were tired. They had traveled many days over dusty roads from their village to the city of Bethlehem. They were worried, too, because many travelers were in the city, and they could find no place to stay. At each place the innkeeper told them, 'Move on! There is no room here for you.' "

Gopal looked at the pictured Mary and Joseph. He knew how they felt, having to move on when they were tired and hungry. Today his family had had to do this, too.

As Gopal heard the rest of the story, he was glad the little family found a place to shelter them. He was glad the baby Jesus was comfortable in the manger. He was glad that the baby grew up to be a strong young man and that he preached to the people about a God who was like a loving Father.

At the end of the story some of the other listeners reached for coins and gave them to the storyteller. In return he gave each one a picture for his own. Gopal wished he had a coin to pay for a picture to show Father and Mother. But he would tell them the story. He remembered the words of the story.

The story man now put more pictures on the table. But before Gopal could move closer to see them, the laughing, swinging group of dancers appeared

28

and caught him up in their turning, twirling circle. As the crowd moved together, they brushed against the table and knocked some of the pictures off it and into a heap at Gopal's feet. Gopal quickly scooped up the pictures in both hands and, holding them safely, moved along with the dancers. When at last he was free from the group, he was far away from the edge of the grassy slope. The storyteller and his table were nowhere to be seen.

"I'll keep the pictures for him," Gopal said to himself. He spread them out in front of him on the ground and examined each one.

A passer-by stopped beside him. Another stopped, then another. Seeing that these people were interested in the pictures, Gopal held up one of them. Just as the storyteller had done, he turned it this way and that, so it could be seen from all sides.

Then he began to repeat the story he had heard. "In all the town this Mary and Joseph could find no place to stay. At every place the innkeeper told them, 'Move on, move on, move on. There's no room here for you. Go find another place.'"

After hearing the story, the listeners moved away. Others came, and again Gopal told the story of the night that Jesus was born. These listeners paid him coins, and to each of them he gave a picture as he had seen the storyteller do. The listeners drifted away, looking at their pictures. Now only one picture remained. Gopal glanced up from it. There near him was the storyteller, carrying his table and music box!

Gopal went to him and gave him the picture and the coins. The young man smiled. "You tell my story very well," he said. "Here, you may keep the picture for yourself."

Gopal reached out and took it with both hands. "Oh, it's my piece of good luck! I'll hold on to it. I won't let it go."

Sitting beside the young man near the table, Gopal told him about all the bad luck that had followed the family on their way to the festival town. "The god sent it because he was angry with us."

The young man shook his head. "No," he said. "Your father's fever came back because he began the journey when he still felt tired. Your mother turned her ankle because she was not careful where she walked. You got lost because you did not remember your father's directions. The god in the temple did not send your bad luck. He is only a statue carved out of stone."

"Tell me more about the God that Jesus preached about," Gopal said. "What does he send?"

"That God is a God of love," the young man answered. "He cares about people and helps them understand what to do. Come to my table tomorrow, and I'll tell you more about him."

Gopal stood up. "I'll go now. I'll take my piece of good luck to Father and Mother. Tomorrow I'll find you again and hear more."

Holding the picture safely in his hands, Gopal hurried off to where his mother and father were waiting.

NEW WORDS IN THE STORY

| garum chai | GAH-room chah-ee | Gopal | GOH-pahl |
| jalebis | jah-LAY-bees | | |

3

Beyond the Bamboo Fence

In the small house in Pakistan where Shama lived with Grandfather and Grandmother there were no books, not even one. And eight-year-old Shama wished for a book. She wanted to learn to read the words that she and Grandfather and Grandmother and all the villagers spoke.

Grandmother always said, "Whoever heard of a girl reading? I've learned what I know by living long years, not by reading. What you need to know, ask! I'll tell you."

Grandfather agreed. "It's no use for a girl to read. Reading doesn't keep the house clean. Reading doesn't bring my *halva* from the sweetshop."

Yet Grandfather was proud that he could read printed words and understand them. Not many people in the village could do this.

So Shama did not learn to read. Instead, each day while Grandfather worked in the sandal shop, Shama and Grandmother worked at home. They swept the floors. They put the beds out to air in the sunny courtyard. They shined the copper pots. And when the house was in order they went to the market.

In the market Grandmother bought some lentils, flour, onions, red peppers, and spices to use when she cooked the family's dinner. Shama went to the sweetmaker's and bought *halva* for Grandfather.

Shama liked to look at the pretty strips of colored paper that decorated the sweetmaker's shop. She liked to watch them blow in the breeze when the sweetmaker waved his wide, palm-branched fan back and forth across the sweets, to keep the flies away.

There were many kinds of sweets—fried *purees*, small puffed up balls; round *laddus* in silver paper wrapping; *pakeras*, crisp, brown, and tasty; *jalebis* oozing with juicy sweetness; and pieces of *halva*, which slid down so easily in eating. Grandfather must have *halva* every day to eat with his dinner.

Almost every day there was time for Shama to play, too. Sometimes she and her friend Jameela skipped rope in the courtyard or played jacks with pebbles. Sometimes they played ball and chanted song words as they bounced the ball in turn.

> On, my ball,
> Go on bouncing!
> Go on, my ball,
> Bounce! Bounce! Bounce!

Sometimes they ran out along the winding path across the wheat fields and stopped to watch the blindfolded oxen walking round and round, making the wooden wheel turn. The turning wheel brought water up from the well and sent it out across the field for the thirsty green shoots to drink.

One day while Shama and Jameela were bouncing their ball in the courtyard, the strange sound of a ringing bell came across the wheat fields.

Tun . . . tun . . .
Tun . . . tun . . .
Tunnn . . . nnn . . . .

Shama, curious, stopped her sing-song bouncing. "Hark! Listen! What is this bell? Who's ringing it?"

Jameela, impatient, answered, "I don't know. Now you've lost your turn. Give me the ball."

Shama continued to listen and wait. When the bell rang again, she cried, "Let's go find it!"

In another moment, with Jameela close behind her, Shama was running along the path, past the oxen and turning wheel, past a shady grove, on and on in the direction of the bell sound. Coming at last to a high bamboo fence, Shama and Jameela stopped. On the other side of the fence they heard a woman's voice. Could this lady have rung the bell? Why had she rung it?

Shama and Jameela stood on tiptoe to see what was beyond the fence, but they were not tall enough to look over it. They clearly heard the lady's words. What she was saying sounded like a story! The lady must be a teacher! They listened.

"Then a Samaritan, as he journeyed, came to where the hurt man was; and when he saw him, he went to him and bound up his wounds. . . . "

Without missing a single word, Shama and Jameela crept quietly along the fence until they found a hole in it. They peeped through. Girls were sitting on the ground beside the lady. A bell and a book were in front of her. This must be a school!

Still listening, the two moved farther along the fence to an opening. They squeezed through it and took their places on the ground near the other girls.

The teacher greeted them with a smile as she continued to tell the story. ". . . And the next day at the inn he took out some coins and gave them to the innkeeper saying, 'Take care of the hurt man, and whatever more you spend, I will repay you when I come back.'"

That was the end of the story. Some of the children spoke out. "Now the hurt man is safe."

Shama wished that she and Jameela had come sooner and had heard all the story. She wished they knew how the poor man had got hurt.

But now the teacher was holding up the book and the bell. "Come again when the bell rings," she invited. "In my Bible are many more stories, which I will tell you."

Later, at home, Shama told Grandfather and Grandmother about hearing the bell and finding the teacher and children on the other side of the bamboo fence. "Her book has many stories," she said.

Grandfather was thoughtful. "I think it is a Christian book the teacher reads. I do not know much about the school, but the Christian religion is different from ours. Do not go there again."

The next day when the bell sounded, Shama and Jameela were playing again in the courtyard. "Come!" cried Jameela. "We'll go to school."

Shama shook her head. "I cannot go. Grandfather says no."

"You must tease him," Jameela said. "At first my father said I could not go. Then I teased and teased, and now he says I may."

Shama said nothing. She knew that this was not the way to get Grandfather's permission. So while

Jameela ran off to school, Shama went instead to the
sweetmaker's shop to watch the blowing streamers
and to buy *halva* for Grandfather.

On this day, as Shama carried the package toward
home, she noticed that the wrapping was not the
usual wide green leaf. This wrapping was paper. It
was covered with strange black marks.

At dinner when Grandfather reached for his
sweet, he, too, noticed the paper wrapping and the

strange black marks. With a grunt of surprise, he spread the paper out on the low wooden stool beside him and examined the marks.

After a long while, Grandfather announced to Shama and Grandmother, "What my eyes read here seems right and good. But it is a new thought to me. 'You shall love your neighbor as yourself.' Only a person with much love in his heart could do this. Few think about their neighbors with love."

To Shama Grandfather said, "Tomorrow when the sweetmaker wraps my piece of *halva,* ask him to put it into another sheet of the printed paper."

The next day Shama did as Grandfather had directed. "Yes," the sweetmaker nodded. "I can do this. I have more of the paper." And getting a piece of it, he wrapped it around the freshly made *halva.*

Today on the way home Shama turned the package this way and that, examining the black marks. She wished she could read the marks and know what they told. But only Grandfather would know whether these marks were like those on the other paper.

In his shop Grandfather could not stop to examine

the paper. He first must finish his work. Later, at home, he must finish eating before he looked at the marks. To Shama the waiting was hard, but finally Grandfather spread out the paper and looked at it carefully.

Soon he read aloud, " 'If any one would be first, he must be last of all and servant of all. . . .' This is strange," he said. "To be first because you are last, to be first because you act as a servant. I wonder— I wonder what it means."

Suddenly Grandfather got up and beckoned to Shama. "Come. We'll go together to the sweetmaker's shop and ask for more of the paper."

At the shop the sweetmaker recognized Shama. "If it is another piece of *halva* you want to buy, I am sorry. Every piece is gone for today."

Grandfather explained, "We have not come for *halva*. We want more of the printed paper."

From the shelf the sweetmaker brought the few remaining pages that once had been a book. He put them into Grandfather's hand. "Good fortune is yours. This much I still have."

"Will you sell these pages to me? Where did you get the book?" asked Grandfather.

The sweetmaker was puzzled. "Is the book important? I did not know. I cannot read. A man sold it to me for a few coins. Where else could I get such cheap wrapping paper?"

Grandfather gave some coins to the sweetmaker in payment for the pages. Then he and Shama hastened home. At home Shama and Grandmother sat with Grandfather and watched his fingers turn the pages of the book and his eyes move across the strange black marks.

"It is a story," Grandfather said after he had finished reading. "It tells about a man who was traveling a lonely road and fell among robbers. They stripped him and beat him and ran away leaving him half-dead. A priest was going down that lonely road, and when he saw the hurt man he passed by on the other side. A second priest came there, and he, too, passed by. Then a Samaritan came, and when he saw the hurt man he went to him. . . ."

"That's the end of the page," Grandfather said.

But Shama cried out, "Oh, Grandfather! The Samaritan helps the hurt traveler. I know! I know! It's the teacher's story, the story I heard by the fence." And Shama told the story's happy ending.

Grandfather said, "Then these pages I have bought must be from a Christian book. All I have read from it tells about good ways to act. There must be goodness in the Christian religion, too."

When the bell sounded again across the fields, Grandfather found Shama playing alone. "You may go to the school," he told her. "Tell the teacher you have come to hear more stories. Perhaps one day you may learn to read them. One day we may have this Christian book for our own."

In a moment Shama was hurrying to join Jameela in the school beyond the bamboo fence.

New Words in the Story

halva	HAL-vah	pakeras	pah-KEH-rahs
jalebis	jah-LAY-bees	purees	POO-rees
Jameela	jah-MEE-lah	Shama	SHAH-mah
laddus	lahd-doos		

4

The Hole in the Reef

On that long-ago day, it was Uriel's turn to be lookout. With a run and a jump, he leaped high and threw his arms around the trunk of the tall coconut tree. Then, hand over hand, bare foot over bare foot, he scurried to the top.

From the ground, Uriel's friends eagerly watched his swift climb. On other days, they, too, had taken turns as lookout from the top of this highest tree on their beautiful island home far out in the Pacific Ocean. Other turns would also come—unless—unless it happened that Uriel today called out the news that they had been long awaiting.

High in the tree, Uriel did not look down at his

waiting friends nor at their thatched-roof homes nor at the school that stood close to the water's edge. He sent down not even one glance at the quiet waters of the lagoon that surrounded the island nor at the jagged coral reef that circled the lagoon far out and separated it from the rough ocean waves beyond.

Instead, Uriel's sharp eyes looked out past the green of the island trees, past the lagoon, past the reef, to the distant, dim, gray line where sky and water came together. Slowly they turned toward the north, then east, south, and west.

But Uriel did not see what he had hoped for. No sail showed against the clear, bright skies.

Disappointed, Uriel called to the waiting boys below, "No ship!"

They murmured in reply, "No Bibles!"

By the time Uriel had dropped easily to the ground, the report was known to every family on the island.

Later, at home, as Uriel worked with Father cutting strips of thick coconut leaves and twisting the heavy fibers into strong lengths of rope, he asked the question he had already asked many times. "When will the ship come?"

And Father's answer was the same he had given to Uriel many times before. "I do not know. Soon, I hope."

For in those days, a hundred years ago, a ship called at the small island but once a year, and the time of its coming was not sure.

Uriel well remembered the ship's last visit more than a year before. It had anchored in the ocean waters beyond the reef. In small rowboats, officers and sailors had daringly ridden the waves over a low spot in the reef to bring medicine, flour, and other supplies across the lagoon to the island people.

After the islanders had welcomed their visitors, an old man had told them about the trouble that had come to them in the past year. "We had only three Bibles in our own language. Now two of them have been ruined. One was eaten by rats and one destroyed by fire. Today the teacher's Bible is the only one that remains. What shall we do if anything happens to it?"

"How can we walk in the ways of God, if we have no Bible to guide us?" asked another man.

The officers had promised, "When we come again, we will bring a chest filled with Bibles, a Bible for each island family."

Now a year had passed, and the ship was long overdue. Young and old alike worried over it and talked about it.

"Perhaps the ship is not coming this year."

"Perhaps it was lost at sea."

"Perhaps the officers have forgotten the promise they made."

But no one could hurry the ship. Each person could only watch and wait, and while they waited, life on the island went on as usual.

Every day Uriel and his friends splashed and played in the warm waters of the lagoon. Sometimes they skillfully caught colored fish that darted by. Often they dived deep and brought up bright shells from the bottom.

47

At school they studied numbers and reading, and listened while the teacher told stories from the Bible and taught them verses to say or sing. Almost every day some islander came to the school to leaf through the pages of the Bible, reading the well-loved words or searching for a forgotten passage. Uriel understood more and more why Father called this book the island's best treasure.

At home, Uriel gathered big leaves for Mother and watched her wrap them around the fish for cooking.

With Father he went fishing in the blue lagoon. On days when the wind was right, they put up the sail on their canoe and went out to the reef to fish. One day when they were on it, they threw out the nets to catch large fish from the ocean side of the reef. Father pointed to a deep crack along the edge of the reef. "Be careful," he said. "Remember that at this place the waves have made a large hole in the reef."

Later when Uriel began to tug and pull on the filled nets to haul them in, he forgot Father's warning. He stumbled and fell into the dark, narrow hole, and the water closed over his head. Uriel held his breath and struggled hard to free himself, but one of his legs was caught.

Father stretched himself out along the reef. He reached his strong arms down into the opening and seized hold of Uriel's uplifted hands. Holding them fast, he slowly pulled the boy up from the jagged hole and landed him on the reef, scratched and bruised and frightened. Father and Uriel took their fish and went back home.

In time, Uriel's scratches and bruises healed, but his fear of the reef remained. Now when Father wanted to fish from the reef, he went alone. Uriel stayed at home.

So the days passed, with play and school and fishing in the lagoon.

There came a day when again it was Uriel's turn to watch for the ship. He climbed the tree slowly, with little hope of seeing anything on the horizon. But when he got to the top, he gave a sharp cry. There before him he saw the long-awaited ship, riding the

ocean waves toward the island. His cry, "The ship! The Bibles!" was at once taken up by the boys waiting below. Uriel dropped quickly from the tree, and by then every island family had heard the news.

Boys and girls ran to the water's edge. Women stopped their cooking and came to look out across the lagoon. Men climbed into canoes and hastened toward the reef, over which the great waves were rolling in a white line of foam.

Father called to Uriel, "Come! We'll go and welcome the sailors!"

But Uriel answered, "No. I'll stay on shore."

So Father did not go out either but waited with Mother on the shore near his canoe, while Uriel climbed again to his perch high in the tree.

From there, Uriel saw the ship anchor in the safety of the deep water beyond the reef. He watched as three small rowboats were lowered from it and started toward the reef. In the third rowboat was a big wooden chest. Uriel smiled. The sailors had not forgotten their promise! The Bibles must be inside the big chest.

The first boat, bringing the medical officer and medical supplies, slipped over a low spot in the reef on the crest of a great wave and slid smoothly into the lagoon. Islanders in canoes and along the shore shouted their welcome with loud cheers. The second boat with its supplies of food also rode in safely.

Uriel's eager eyes were fastened on the third small boat with its precious Bibles, one for every island family. But as he watched, he turned stiff with alarm. His mind could not believe what his eyes saw! The third boat failed to slide over the reef. It whirled in wide circles, then struck the reef once, twice, and overturned, sending chest and sailors into the churning sea.

The sailors quickly climbed onto the reef, caught the boat, and righted it. The chest floated free, bobbing in the waves. The eager sailors reached for it as it was swept forward on a wave, and tried to float it over the reef into the lagoon. But the wave rushed by and, as Uriel watched, the chest disappeared from sight. It was caught, trapped in a hole on the reef—the same jagged hole Uriel knew so well.

The islanders joined the sailors on the reef. In the frothing water they pushed and shoved at the chest, only to wedge it deeper and tighter into the hole. The officer in command roared out an order, which Uriel heard from where he sat in the tree. "We need a small boy—a brave one—and a length of heavy rope. Bring them swiftly."

Uriel's body scarcely moved, but his mind moved quickly. He of all the island boys knew best what the hole was like. He was the one to go to the reef, to climb down, and to save the chest. He must do it even though he was afraid.

Dropping from the tree, Uriel ran home and picked up the newest rope he and Father had made from the strong coconut fibers. Father was standing beside his canoe at the water's edge.

Out on the reef, the men were silent as Father and Uriel drew near and climbed out of the canoe. Father tied one end of the rope securely around Uriel's waist. Uriel lowered himself part way into the hole. He took one last deep breath and carefully squeezed past the edge of the chest, with the rope trailing behind him. He was thinking too hard about how to get through the narrow passage to feel afraid any more. In the watery darkness he felt his way until he was beneath the chest. Then he came up on the other side —up toward the light and air and Father's strong arms that were waiting for him and for the rope that now encircled the chest.

A sailor untied the rope from Uriel's waist, took both ends of it, and pulled it tightly around the chest. Other sailors grabbed the ends, and with a mighty jerk upwards and outwards, they floated the chest free. A bouncing wave quickly carried it over the reef and into the lagoon. There it was placed in the righted boat, and a long line of cheering islanders in canoes followed their Bibles to shore.

That very evening the chest was opened, and inside were the precious Bibles, each book safe and dry in the tight, waterproof chest.

"Uriel must lift out the first book," said an old man. The people nodded. "He helped rescue the chest, and he must have the first Bible for his own."

5

The Name That Was Different

Lydia liked her name. Not one of her friends in the Guatamalan village where she lived had a name so pretty. There was Carmen! And Carlita, María, and Felice! There was Tina! And Teresa, Luisa, and Pepita! But there was only one Lydia. Six-year-old Lydia's papá said that in all the country around he had never heard of anyone with a name like hers.

Lydia liked the small white adobe house where she, Papá, and Mamá lived, too. It stood at the edge of the village. A garden with growing vegetables was beside the house. A well with cool, clear water to drink was beside the garden. Bright flowers grew near the gate at the end of the path.

When villagers stopped at the gate to talk with Papá and Mamá or came into the house for a visit, they smiled at Lydia and told her, "You have a pretty name."

Lydia always smiled back and said, "My name's in the Bible." The visitors knew this was true.

When strangers traveled along the path and saw Lydia and Mamá in the garden, they sometimes stopped and asked directions to the village, the market town, or the coffee plantation beyond. Sometimes they added, "What is your name, little girl?"

Lydia always answered, "Lydia. My name's in the Bible."

The Bible was an important book to Papá, Mamá, and Lydia. Selling Bible pictures and copies of the Gospels and telling Bible stories was Papá's work.

Every morning he took down the strong leather bag from its hook on the wall. Then from the box on the special shelf by the door where the family kept its treasures, he took the Gospels and the Bible pictures and papers. He put them into the bag and then trudged off down the path, going to sell them in the nearby villages and the market town beyond. Some buyers looked at the pictures and read the printed words for themselves. Others waited for Papá to explain them.

Sometimes Lydia helped Papá to fold the papers and put them into the strong bag. Often she begged, "Let me go with you. Let me help carry the bag."

Papá always said, "No. Your small hands are not yet strong enough for big things—only for little ones."

Sometimes Mamá said the same thing. The time Lydia begged to help scoop out the squash to make cups and bowls for the family's use, Mamá said, "No, your hands are not strong enough for big things—only for little ones."

So every day Lydia watched Papá go alone through the gate carrying the strong bag filled with pictures and papers. Every day she watched Mamá work alone, gathering the vegetables from the garden and patting the corncakes by the doorway, making them ready for cooking. Lydia wished her hands were big enough right now to do big things.

Every day Lydia played in the yard and waited for

Papá to return. Sometimes she found a surprise and had it ready for him. Once the surprise was a bright feather from under the tree. Once it was a smooth stone from along the path. Many times it was a pretty flower from near the gate. When Papá saw the surprise, he always said, "*Gracias!* Thank you!"

Sometimes in return Papá gave Lydia a small coin to be her very own. This she dropped into her bright orange-colored clay bird, which stood on the shelf beside Papá's box of Bible pictures and papers. When there were enough coins inside the bird, Lydia could buy sweets and new ribbons for herself.

Sometimes in return for the surprise Papá said, "Come, sit beside me on the bench while I rest. I will tell you a story about what you have brought me."

Lydia liked stories. Often when Papá finished such a story, Lydia said, "Now please tell me about the Lydia in the Bible."

The story of the lady whose name was like her own was Lydia's favorite. Papá always began it the same way. "Friendly Lydia lived long ago in a faraway country." Then he continued, "Lydia visited lonely people. She helped those in trouble. She shared her home with tired travelers."

Papá always ended the story the same way. "Small daughter, Mamá and I think you will grow up to act in the same friendly way that Lydia did long ago. That is why we gave you her name."

Often Lydia thought, "But how can I grow up to be like Lydia? Papá and Mamá say my hands can do only little things."

One day when Papá came from work he called to Lydia and Mamá, "Today I have brought the surprise! These pictures came in my new supply of story pictures. Look!" Papá took a picture from the package and together he, Mamá, and Lydia looked at it. "It is the Lydia of the Bible! Her friends are beside her. She is giving them something to eat."

Lydia seemed to see everything in the picture at once, and she talked about what she saw. "Lydia's house is white like ours. She wears sandals and a blue dress. And why are the people's clothes different from ours?"

Papá tried to explain everything in the picture—

the flat-roofed house, the long, loose clothing, the headdresses, the copper bowls.

Lydia looked again at the pictured Lydia. "How can I grow up to be friendly like her?" she wondered.

The next morning when Papá packed his day's supply of Bible pictures and papers, Lydia put in some of the new picture stories of Lydia. Then she and Mamá walked to the gate with Papá.

"*Adiós!*" They waved good-by as Papá went on his way. Then as Lydia stopped to pick some of the flowers near the gate, Mamá noticed that the earth around them was hard and dry.

"Daughter, the flowers need a drink," she said.

From the well Mamá brought a jug of water. From the house Lydia brought a gourd cup.

Then Mamá went to sit at her work in the doorway, while Lydia started to water the flowers. She dipped out the cool water with the cup and poured it around the plants to soak down to their thirsty roots. One gourdful of water, then another and another she emptied out around the flowers. As she was about to fill the gourd again, a strange voice called from beyond the gate, "*Hola!* Hello! Little girl, my small burro needs a drink."

Lydia looked up. An old man astride a sturdy little donkey had stopped beside the gate. A basket of vegetables was tied in place behind him.

"My good donkey has carried me many miles since early sun," he said. "We must travel many more miles to reach my daughter's home across the mountain. Now, my burro needs a drink."

"You are welcome to water for him," Mamá said from the doorway.

Lydia filled the gourd brimming full and handed the water up to the traveler. "A drink for you, too."

After drinking the water, the old man dismounted and led his burro through the gate into the yard. Mamá brought a pan, which the old man filled with water from the jug. His burro drank it all.

Bowing his thanks, the traveler climbed astride his burro. Suddenly he turned to Lydia. "What is your name, little one? I must tell it to my daughter."

"Lydia. My name's in the Bible."

Leaning forward, the old man quickly dropped a

coin into Lydia's hand. "My coins are few, but this will buy a sweet for you."

"*Gracias!*" Lydia thanked the old man. Then before he could pick up the reins and trot away she added, "Wait, please!"

Turning, she ran quickly into the house. In a moment she was back and handed up to the old man one of Papá's new pictures. "It's Lydia," she said and pointed to the printed words beneath. "The story tells about her."

The old man tucked the picture into his pocket. Waving his hand and calling a cheery, "Until I come again," he was on his way.

That night when Papá came from the village, Lydia told him about the traveler, the burro, and the picture. When she gave him the coin, she said, "It's for the Lydia picture."

Papá said, "You may keep it. Put it into your bird."

Not many days later, the old man and his burro appeared again in the path. This time he was traveling in the opposite direction. Stopping at the gate he called, "*Hola!* Hello! My small burro needs a drink."

Mamá and Lydia in the garden heard the greeting and came to the gate. Mamá said, "You are welcome to water for your thirsty burro."

Lydia added, "And for you, too! Come. I'll show you where to get it."

Following Mamá and Lydia to the well, the old man poured water into the pan for his burro. Lydia filled the gourd cup and handed it to the old man for himself.

Finishing his drink, the old man seemed in no

hurry to leave. "Lydia, small one, my daughter read to me the printed words on the picture you brought to me. Your mamá and papá gave you a good name. I see this for myself." Then, as the old man climbed onto his burro, he continued, "Soon I will take more vegetables to my daughter. I will stop then for another paper. We have never heard such stories as these."

That night when Papá returned from work, Lydia was waiting. This time she had no surprise. Instead, she put her clay bird into Papá's hand. "Hear my money," she said, rattling the coins inside the bird. "Papá, please count it."

Papá emptied the coins from the bright little bird and spread them on the table—one—two—three—four—five. "You have enough for many sweets and ribbons," he said.

"No! I don't want anything from the market!" Lydia said, "It's for a Gospel from your bag, a Gospel for the old man. He will like it."

Papá went to the box on the shelf and from it took a new Gospel. He gave it to Lydia. "Lydia, small daughter, you do not need big hands to do big things."

Lydia put the Gospel in place on the special shelf, safe between the empty bird and Papá's box. Every day after that she watched and listened for the familiar call at the gate—"*Hola!* Hello! My small burro needs a drink."

When she heard it, she ran quickly to the gate.

She had the water ready for the burro. Before the old man left, she went into the house and got the Gospel. When she came back, she handed it to him. He thanked her many times. Lydia watched him ride away, holding the book as if it were a treasure.

New Words in the Story

adiós	ah-dee-OHS	Mamá	mah-MAH
Carlita	kar-LEE-tah	María	mah-REE-ah
Carmen	KAR-men	Papá	pah-PAH
Felice	fay-LEE-say	Pepita	pay-PEE-tah
gracias	GRAH-see-ahs	Teresa	tay-RAY-sah
hola	OH-lah	Tina	TEE-nah
Luisa	loo-EE-sah		

6

The Neglected Garden

Eyenga walked with a limp. Her leg was twisted. The leg had always been twisted. No one in the African village—least of all Eyenga herself—ever thought it might some day be straight.

Having a twisted leg mattered very much to Eyenga. Because of it she always had to walk slowly. And more than anything else Eyenga wanted to run, skip, jump, and climb and be like the other children. But even though she could not do everything they did, still she could be a good friend to them.

So at playtime when Menge, Ava, and the others called, "Come, let's play!" Eyenga answered happily, "I'm coming!" And almost always she found a way to join their fun and to show them that she wanted to be with them.

When the game was played in a circle, Eyenga offered, "I'll beat the rhythm for you." She sat in the center and clapped her hands while the players did the actions in time to the rhythm.

When the children stopped on the way from school to play hopscotch, Eyenga said, "I'll hold your books." She sat beside the path and watched the books and pencils while the others played.

The children loved having Eyenga with them. "Eyenga," they told her, "your name means 'pal' and you ARE a pal."

At the mission school where the children went every day, Eyenga's twisted leg also mattered. Eyenga could not balance herself well enough to hold the heavy bar and strike it against the swinging bar to signal that lessons were beginning. But she liked to watch when the teacher permitted the other children to strike the bar.

Eyenga tired quickly if she stood at the black-board to work the arithmetic sums. So she worked them at her own bench and tried to be content. When the choir stood to sing, Eyenga sang the songs from where she sat. She remembered the tunes and words well. And she remembered the Bible stories and verses the teacher read to the class. Often as she walked back and forth to school with the children she helped them to remember these, too.

The children told Eyenga, "Oh, you're the smart one!" They meant it, too. They were proud of Eyenga's friendliness, her quickness, her good memory. They felt a gladness inside themselves because their praise pleased Eyenga.

One morning the iron bar that rang to call the children to their lessons clanged its sound out louder than usual. It also clanged longer.

That morning when the children went out toward school, they did not stop as usual to listen to the hammering in the new white doctor's house or to wade in the cool forest stream. They hurried—at least Menge, Ava, and the others hurried. Eyenga limped along and tried to keep up. The teacher would have important news today.

The teacher told his news at once. "The Governor of our country is coming soon to our village! Every yard must be clean. Every house must have fresh whitewash. Paths and gardens must be weeded." During their lessons that day the children talked about the Governor's visit and ways to make the village ready for him.

A few mornings later as the children walked to school past the chief's house, the new doctor's house, other houses, the forest stream, and the garden plots at the far edge of the village, they examined every yard. They looked closely at every house.

"See! The chief's house has fresh whitewash."

"The white doctor's front door has a new latch."

"This yard is swept clean."

"Every weed in this yard has been cut."

The village was getting ready, and all that the children saw pleased them—that is, it did until they came to the garden plots. There Eyenga's quick glance and sharp eyes noticed one garden almost hidden from sight beyond the others.

"Look!" she pointed. "The fence is broken. Weeds

are everywhere. Spoiled pineapples and broken cornstalks are on the ground. What villager would let his garden look like this?"

Yes, this garden was indeed neglected and ugly. Who in the village could be so careless?

At school, the children reported to the teacher what they had seen. Eyenga described the neglected garden. Everyone asked, "Whose garden is it?"

The teacher thought for a moment. "Why, I think it must be the plot planted last year by Evina, who moved away. This means it now belongs to the man who lives in Evina's house—the new white doctor."

The children were still curious.

"Then why doesn't the doctor tend the garden?"

"Doesn't he know everything is spoiling?"

"Doesn't he know the Governor is coming?"

The teacher said, "He has been very busy since he came to the village. A doctor's work is never finished, you know."

"I know," Menge said, "because every day the doctor rides his motorbike out to other villages. In the next village he gives medicine to my sick uncle."

Ava said, "Every day I hear hammering inside the doctor's house. The chief says workmen are pounding down a fresh mud floor. And other workmen are building plank beds and rows of shelves."

Eyenga spoke up. "Maybe the doctor doesn't know that the garden is his. Maybe no one told him."

Menge said, "Then somebody ought to tell him. We could tell him."

That day after lessons were finished and the children were on their way home, they stopped in the shade of a nearby tree. They talked about the doctor and the garden.

Eyenga said, "We must tell the doctor today. The garden will go back to bush if he doesn't take care of it soon."

"Yes," the others agreed. "Nothing can grow among so many weeds."

But who would go to the doctor's door?

The children looked to Eyenga for an answer because she always knew what to do. Eyenga said, "The two oldest ones." So when the children came to the doctor's house, these two walked bravely toward his wide-open door. Eyenga and the others waited and watched at a distance.

At the door the two visitors listened for the hammering, but they heard no sounds. They called out, "We are here." When no one answered the call, the children looked beyond the door. They had never seen such a room. It smelled clean with fresh whitewash. Shelves along the walls reached from ceiling to floor. Bottles and boxes filled the shelves. Through another door they saw beds, each with a tent of mosquito netting in place over it.

The visitors were about to call out again when the doctor's houseboy appeared. He did not wait for them to speak. He did not ask the reason for the visit. "No clinic today," he announced gruffly. "Don't bother the doctor. He's busy now."

The children went back to the waiting ones. They told what they had seen. "We'll go again tomorrow. Maybe the doctor won't be busy then."

The next afternoon the children talked again.

"Even if the doctor knows about the garden, hoeing isn't a doctor's business."

"He could hire a woman to do it. Gardening is woman's work."

"Or children's work."

"But he has no children."

"How sad when a man has no children! But then the doctor doesn't even have a wife."

Eyenga spoke up. "I know! We could clear the garden for the doctor. And tell him after it is done."

Menge liked the idea. "Yes, he does good for my sick uncle—for all the sick people. We could do good for him."

The others liked the idea. "We could work a little while every day after school."

"I'll bring my hoe and chop down the weeds."

"I'll bring mine, too."

"I'll mend the fence."

Eyenga knew how she could help. "I'll sit on the ground and pick up all the weeds and stack them in piles. We'll ask the teacher to come and burn them."

The next afternoon the children began their work. Some days later, when the garden plot was cleared, they went together to the doctor's house.

This time, the houseboy heard their happy, excited voices on the path. Believing the children to be up to some mischief, he called out to them in an annoyed, angry voice, "If you've come to grab the ripe oranges off the doctor's tree, it's no use. I'm watching. I'll tell the doctor when he comes home."

Before the children could reply, the putt-putt-putt of a motor sounded, and the doctor himself whizzed up the path on his motorbike. He looked in surprise from his visitors to the houseboy. "What is it you will tell the doctor?" he asked, but there was no answer. The houseboy had disappeared from sight.

The children gathered around the doctor. Their words tumbled out eagerly.

"It's about your garden, sir."

"Your garden is cleared."

"Your plants are growing."

"The weeds are cut."

"The fence is mended."

The doctor did not understand. "What's this? What's this? What's this you say? I have no garden. I've been too busy."

"You live in Evina's house, so Evina's garden is yours."

"He planted it before he moved."

"But it was going back to bush."

Still the doctor was puzzled. "Where is this garden? I'd like to see it."

"Come. We'll show you." The children ran ahead to lead the way, all except Eyenga. She limped along trying to keep up with the others.

For the first time the doctor noticed her twisted leg. "You'll ride with me," he said, running after her. He lifted her up behind him on the seat of the motorbike. Soon the children, doctor, Eyenga, and motorbike were past the village houses, past the forest stream, and out beside the garden plots.

"Here!" the children said, pointing to the cleared plot with its many plants growing green and straight.

"So this is what you've been doing for me!" The doctor was pleased.

"Yes!" Menge's voice was pleased, too. "You do good to people. We thought we'd do good to you."

"You surprised me," the doctor said. "Now I want

76

to make a surprise for you." He turned to Eyenga. "Tomorrow, ask your mother to bring you to the clinic. I want to examine that twisted leg. I think I can operate on it and make it as strong and as straight as the other one."

And the very next week, the day after the Governor's visit, when Eyenga opened her eyes in the hospital, the operation was over! "Can I run now?" she asked the doctor.

"Not today. Not tomorrow," the doctor answered. "But one day you will. You'll also jump and skip and climb. Your leg needs many weeks to mend itself. While it mends, you must lie still on your bed."

"Can I ring the gong at school?" Eyenga asked.

"Yes," the doctor nodded. "You can do everything the other children can do."

Eyenga didn't need to ask if she could find a way to be a friend. She knew she could do that.

New Words in the Story

Ava	AH-vah	Eyenga	eh-YEH-ngah
Evina	eh-VEE-nah	Menge	MEH-ngeh

7

The Primer

If anyone in Lunon's village in the Philippines had told seven-year-old Lunon, "You're going to write a book," she would not have believed it. Nor would anyone else in the village. Why, Lunon could not read, nor could anyone in the village. And Lunon had never seen a book nor even thought about one. Her thoughts were only about big sister Gumbay and about Grandfather and Grandmother with whom they lived.

But things began to be different the day the strange Americans came to the village. This day, for Lunon, started out much like an ordinary day. The sun, round and bright, came up to show above the distant mountain. Its brightness shone into her small house, which stood high off the ground on its four sturdy poles. And it reached the spot where Lunon was asleep, and fell on her eyes and wakened her.

From her mat Lunon heard sounds of cooking and talking. She heard Grandfather hurrying down the steps of the bamboo ladder that led from the high porch to the ground below. Grandfather was headman of the village. He must be early about his work. All day villagers would bring him their hard questions to answer, their quarrels to settle.

Lunon could stay still no longer. She got up and ate the breakfast that was ready. When she had finished, Grandmother said, "There is washing and cleaning to be done today."

Gumbay said, "I'll get the clothes ready and put them in bundles."

Lunon said, "I'll sweep." She took the broom from the corner. For a few minutes she was very busy. Then she told Grandmother, "The floor is clean."

Grandmother examined the bare floorboards. Yes, the dirt was indeed gone. Lunon had pushed it out of sight through the cracks between the wide boards to fall to the ground below.

Gumbay told Lunon, "Come now with me. We'll wash the clothes at the river." Lunon liked to be with Gumbay, to go where she went.

Lunon picked up the small bundle, balanced it easily on her head, and ran down the slanting ladder. Gumbay followed with the big bundle balanced on her head.

Out past the coconut palm trees and the fiber plants they went and on along the river road. Lunon, scarcely as high as the tall grass growing beside the road, darted to one side, then another, never still. She chattered back to the chattering monkeys. She watched the baby hornbill and laughed to hear him fussing through his big, black bill.

At the river Lunon sat beside Gumbay on a rock in the shallow, swift stream. She dangled her feet in the water. She dangled her fingers in the water. Gumbay dipped the clothing into the water and rubbed each piece clean against the rock.

"I'll help you," offered Lunon. She picked up an

armful of the clean wet clothes and started up the grassy bank to spread them in the sun to dry.

Suddenly the roar of a motorcar rumbled along the road above, and at that moment the day began to be different. Lunon listened. This chug-chug rattle-rattle must be the government jeep! The car from the distant government station rarely traveled to the village, but when it came it usually had important business. It always stopped at Grandfather's house. Every person who had business in the village must first stop to talk with Grandfather. The jeep must be going to him now.

Lunon forgot about helping Gumbay. She dropped the wet clothes in a heap. She ran to the top of the slope, reaching it just as the bright red government jeep flashed past.

"Red jeep!" she called back to Gumbay. Thinking only of the possible excitement ahead, she skipped along the road in the whirls of dust behind the rattling car. In the car she could see nothing except a pile of bags and boxes. These must be for Grandfather. What was inside them?

Now far ahead, the red car pulled to a noisy, jolting stop beside Grandfather's house. Lunon hurried. She ran. In a short while, she, too, stopped beside the house, but out of sight behind one of the four sturdy poles.

She peeped from her place. Already the government man was out of the jeep and beside the ladder. Now, climbing over the boxes and bags and jumping to the ground was a young woman, a white woman. And another one just like this one was still in her seat in the jeep.

The government man called up the ladder, "Hello! Hello!" When there was no answer, he pulled the brass gong hanging beside the ladder. This sounded a signal to Grandfather to come home. He could hear it from any place in the village.

While the three travelers waited for Grandfather to come, they talked together. Lunon could not understand their words. They were different from those spoken by the villagers.

When Grandfather hurried up, he and the government man exchanged polite greetings in the language of the village, and this time Lunon understood every word. Then the government man said, "These two young women have come from America to help you. They want to study your words so they can teach you to read and write them. They have already learned a few of the words of your language, but they want to know all of them. Now they are asking you to give them a home and someone to live with them to help them with their work. The young woman beside the jeep is a teacher. The one inside the jeep is a nurse."

Lunon peeped out again. She could not remember anything like this happening before. What should she do?

Grandfather looked a long time at the two young women. To the government man he said finally, "The American ladies are welcome to live in this village. Take them and their boxes and bags to the empty house beyond the market place. Tomorrow I will bring them my best help. I'll bring my granddaughter Gumbay."

Gumbay! Lunon waited to hear no more. Now she

knew what to do. She turned and sped back along the dusty road to the river. She tumbled down the bank over the clean clothes drying in the sun. She told Gumbay, "Two American ladies have come to live in the village. Tomorrow you go to live in their house to help them. Grandfather said it."

Lunon and Gumbay knew what Grandfather said would be what happened.

The next morning Gumbay made a bundle of her clothes and her sleeping mat. Lunon saw her. She, too, made a bundle of her clothing and mat. Then she spoke out. "I'll go with Gumbay. I'll help the ladies, too."

Grandmother looked surprised. Gumbay was pleased. Grandfather said, "Very well! Gumbay will take care of you." He took Lunon's hand, and the three walked together through the village to the once empty house. Now cheerful voices and laughter sounded out through the door.

Grandfather told the young women, "My grand-daughters—both will help."

In no time at all Lunon and Gumbay found work

to do. "The ladies, I think they know nothing!" giggled Gumbay, and she took the big basket and went to the market to buy corn and rice and to the forest to pick greens to eat.

"The ladies, I think they know nothing!" giggled Lunon, and she took the broom and swept the floor clean, pushing the dirt out of sight through the cracks between the wide boards to fall onto the ground below.

"The ladies, how funny!" giggled Gumbay, who expected to eat her dinner with her fingers and instead was given two shining sticks, one with points on the end and one with a sharp edge on one side.

"The ladies, how funny!" giggled Lunon, who expected her dinner to be put on a wide green leaf and instead found it on a round blue plate that crashed into many pieces when she dropped it onto the floor.

That day and every day, Lunon ran to find Grandfather and Grandmother and to tell them all that had happened.

That night and every night, Lunon and Gumbay unrolled their mats on the floor of the little house and slept close beside the American ladies in their two beds built off the floor on legs.

For many days Lunon and Gumbay worked, helping to unpack the many boxes and bags. They giggled and opened their eyes in wonder at the surprising things they found inside.

One box held strange white powder. The nurse lady put some of it into a bowl. "Water," she said, and Lunon brought water and put it into the bowl. The nurse stirred hard and mixed the powder and the water. "Milk," the nurse said and poured some of the mixture for each girl to drink.

In one box there was a shining square with a wooden frame. The teacher lady hung it on the wall. Lunon went boldly up and stood in front of it the better to see it. A face stared back at her. She screamed, "This girl wears my blouse, my earrings! Where is this girl?" She pushed the shining square aside to look behind it. She ran around to the other side of the wall and looked there.

The teacher lady brought Lunon back. She pointed to the girl in the mirror and said, "Lunon."

For the rest of the day, Lunon returned again and again to the strange shining square to stare at her own strange likeness.

From another box the teacher lady took a book she called "Bible." She put it on the table and looked in it every day. She opened it one day, and Lunon saw small black marks on the pages. She asked, "Do the marks talk to you?"

The teacher lady said, "Yes, the marks talk."

The next day in the yard Lunon found a twig and made scribbles on the ground. She ran for the teacher lady. "See!" she giggled. "The marks talk to me. They say, 'Lunon.'"

The teacher lady held Lunon's hand on the twig and guided it to make new marks. She pointed to the letters—L U N O N. "Lunon," she said.

All the rest of that day Lunon did no work in the house. She did no work of any kind. Instead, she copied the marks over and over again. When she could make them like those the teacher lady had made, she said, "Lunon! Me!" Then she ran to make the marks for Grandfather.

The next day Lunon asked the teacher lady, "Make the marks say 'basket.'" With the twig, the teacher lady wrote *abi* on the ground. "Make 'stove.' Make 'water,'" Lunon begged. She carefully copied each word over and over until it was right. Then she said the words out loud. Soon she knew other words that the teacher lady made—*rice, bed, flower, sun, house.*

"Lunon, you read!" the teacher lady told her. She gave her a pencil and some pieces of paper. With the pencil Lunon marked each word she knew on its own piece of paper. She showed them to Gumbay. "I read!" And she read each one to her. She took them to Grandfather and Grandmother. "I read!" she told them and read each one to them.

One day when Lunon read the word for sun on her paper, she pointed to the sun in the sky and put a round mark on the paper to make a circle like the sun. Soon each word had a matching picture—*basket, flower, Bible, house.*

The teacher lady was pleased. She brought cloth, cut it, and sewed it over the pages for a cover. "Primer," she told Lunon, and printed the word on the cover in Lunon's language.

Lunon carried her book all over the village and read its words to everyone who would listen. At night she put the primer on the teacher lady's table beside the Bible. One day she would read the words from that book, too.

New Words in the Story

Gumbay	GOOM-bye	Lunon	loo-NOHN

8

The Missing Words

Peter was only eight years old, but he could speak three languages.

He lived in Mexico, so of course he could speak Spanish, the language of the country. He learned everyday Spanish words from the traders who traveled on foot and donkeyback up the steep mountain trails to the small scattered villages. From their large baskets mothers bought new clothing, pretty trinkets, and toys.

Peter learned other Spanish words on trips to Mexico City with his mother and father. There he listened to people in railway stations, on streets, in shops and hotels, and he remembered their words.

Peter, Father, and Mother were American, so of course Peter could speak English. The first words he ever spoke were English. The nursery rhymes and stories Father and Mother read to him were in English. Peter, Mother, and Father spoke this language at home. And when Peter returned to the United States and visited Grandmother, he spoke it there.

Peter's third language was Mazateco. Peter, Father, and Mother lived among the Mazateco Indians, so of course he could speak their language. Peter learned Mazateco words from his Mazateco playmates—Emilio, Raimundo, and Esteban. He spoke it whenever he played games with them or visited and ate with them in their homes.

Sometimes in their games, Peter got so excited that words in all three languages tumbled out of his mouth. Then Emilio, Raimundo, and Esteban rolled on the ground and shook with laughter because what they were hearing sounded so strange.

Of all the languages Peter knew, he was sure Mazateco was the most important. "We need Mazateco words for the Bible," Peter told Mother.

Mother said, "Yes, we need all the words that Father and I can learn and all that you can learn, if we are to write Bible stories in words the people will understand."

Writing the Bible in Mazateco words was Father's and Mother's work. They were busy with it day and night. There were so many words to learn, each with its own tone and pitch, that Father sometimes grew discouraged. "I wonder if we'll ever find all the words we need for writing the Bible," he would say.

When Mother went to the market to buy fish and fruit, she learned words. When she stopped at neighbor Camilla's house to see the new baby, she learned words.

Father learned words from curious villagers who talked together while they watched him build shelves and put them into place along the walls and while he put the big books on the shelves.

Each word that Father and Mother learned was printed on a card to be placed in the file box.

Peter learned words, too. When he was with his friends, he listened to all they said at play and at home. Then he repeated the words slowly and carefully until Emilio, Raimundo, and Esteban said in Mazateco what Peter knew to mean O.K. Then he was sure he had pronounced the words in the proper tone and pitch, and that they were ready for Mother to put on cards for the box.

One day after Peter had played marbles with Emilio, he told Mother, "I learned 'circle.' "

Another day after he had played flying kites with Raimundo, he told Mother, "I learned 'wind.' "

One day when he was hungry at Esteban's house, he ate one of the good *tortillas* Esteban's mother had cooked on hot stones. That day Peter told Mother, "I learned, 'I'm not hungry any more.' "

" 'Hungry'!" Mother repeated the word happily and gave Peter a hug. "Why, that is a word that has been missing! Now I can write the story about the boy who shared his lunch with the hungry people."

But on another day Peter played so long with his friends that Mother was worried. When he finally came home, wet and muddy, Mother was about to scold him. Then Peter told her, "I learned another word! We found a spring in the forest and played there. I learned 'spring.'"

So Mother forgot the scolding, said thank you instead, and hurried to print this new word on a card.

Many, many words were printed on Mother's cards, but not all of them were ones needed for the Bible. Getting the correct ones took such a long time that Mother sometimes got discouraged, too. But she always told Peter, "Keep listening and learning, Son. Some day we will find the missing ones."

Peter liked to watch Father and Mother at their work. Emilio, Raimundo, and Esteban often came to watch, too. "That's the dictionary. That's the encyclopedia. That's the Bible," Peter told them as he pointed to Father's big books. The boys only stared.

When Peter opened picture books and magazines and showed his friends bright-colored pictures, they turned the pictures this way and that way, upside down and right side up. To them, either way was interesting.

When the visitors said, "*Si sca!* Let's play!" and pointed to Peter's three toy figures on the shelf, Peter lifted them down onto the floor. Mother had bought the small clay figures for him from the trader's basket, and Peter liked to play with them. He always pretended that one of the little men was Spanish, one was American, and one was Mazateco. He held conversations for the three, speaking in turn for each figure in its own language.

First he picked up the Spanish one and said in Spanish words, *"Buenos días.* Good day." Then quickly he made English words come from the American. "What do you want for breakfast?" Then the Mazateco Indian spoke. *"Nta li.* Hello." And just as they always did when Peter's words tumbled out in all three languages, Emilio, Raimundo, and Esteban rolled on the floor and shook with laughter at the many strange sounds.

Villagers also liked to watch Father and Mother at work. The door to Peter's house was seldom closed, so almost every day one person, or six or ten, came into the room and stayed to watch.

They watched Father look inside the big books and make marks with his little round stick. They

watched Mother strike with her fingers the rows of round buttons along the bottom of her click-click box, as they called the typewriter. They watched the black marks jump out of the box and onto the big white sheet at the top of the box. Sometimes the villagers sat quietly on the floor and seemed to be watching nothing at all.

Neighbor Camilla's hens came to watch, too. They strutted through the door and went at once to stand beside Father's desk. Sometimes they hopped up to the window sill, then flapped their wings and

swooshed to a landing field on top of Father's desk. There they stayed, clucking and fussing and bothering Father until he shooed them away.

Peter told Father, "I know what to do." He brought a handful of small pebbles and lined them up in a row on Father's desk. The next time the hens came to visit, Father threw the stones gently, one at a time, and scared away the intruders without stopping his work.

Peter also found ways to help Mother. He could not offer to straighten the many stacks of papers and notebooks piled here and there around the room. He knew he must never touch those. But when he noticed that Mother was eager to finish the typing she had planned for the day or to copy lists of new words on her filing cards, he would offer, "Today I can bring the fish from the market," or "I can cook the carrots," or "I can set the table."

So day by day, the weeks and months passed. Peter grew older. Father and Mother completed more verses and chapters for the Mazateco Bible. Whenever they finished verses that Peter knew, the family read them together, and the next day Peter told them to Emilio, Raimundo, and Esteban.

One night Father told Peter, "Bring your Bible. Another verse is ready."

Together Peter, Father, and Mother read the English words, " 'Jesus . . . went about doing good.' " Then they read the same words in Mazateco as Father and Mother had translated them.

That night Peter repeated another verse he knew. " 'Jesus called them to him, saying, "Let the children come to me and do not hinder them." ' When will this verse be ready?" he asked. "I want to tell this one to Emilio, Raimundo, and Esteban."

Mother shook her head. "I don't know. We can't seem to discover the right words for this verse."

Father tried to explain. "In all the years we have lived in the village we have not been able to learn the way tribespeople say, 'Do not hinder.' How to express this idea in their language still puzzles us. To keep waiting and watching for missing words when we don't know how to find them is difficult."

Peter understood how it was and how hard Father and Mother were trying.

A few days later, Emilio, Raimundo, and Esteban came in search of Peter, and they all played together in Peter's yard. Esteban announced, "Now we can play 'Guard the Treasure.'" This was a new game to Peter, but he learned the rules quickly.

Esteban placed his ball on the tree stump. "The ball's the treasure," he told Peter. "You and I guard it."

Esteban and Peter stretched out their arms to protect the ball while Emilio and Raimundo dodged, twisted, ducked, and turned as they tried to steal under or around the outstretched arms. To win the game, they had to snatch away the treasure from its place on the stump. They had to get it in any way they could.

"Under!" shouted Emilio in Mazateco.

"Around!" shouted Raimundo.

No matter how hard they tried, they could not reach the ball. Esteban and Peter always had their arms in the right place to keep them away.

Finally Emilio shouted, "Don't block the way!"

Raimundo shouted, "Don't close up the passage!"

Esteban answered, "We must keep you away."

Peter added, "You can't get the treasure."

Just then, before the game could go further, Mother came running from the house straight to the ducking, twisting, turning Emilio and Raimundo. "Those words!" she cried. "Say them exactly as before. Exactly!" Mother had her card ready to write them down.

"Don't block the way," Emilio repeated.

"Don't close up the passage," Raimundo repeated.

Mother was almost too excited to print the words. "These are our missing words! Thank you! Thank you!"

Peter was excited, too. He left the game and followed Mother into the house. In a little while the small clay figures were on the floor beside Peter, each talking to the other through Peter's words.

One said in Mazateco, "Don't block the way. Don't close up the passage."

One said in English, "Thank you! Thank you!"

One said in Spanish, "*Adiós!* Good-by!"

So back they went to their places on the shelf.

The next day it was Peter who went in search of his friends. "Another story," he called. Emilio, Raimundo, and Esteban dropped down to the ground and listened as Peter told the story in their Mazateco words.

"When Jesus lived on earth long ago, he loved all the children. No matter where he was, he liked to have them with him. If the grown people crowded around Jesus and tried to push the children away, Jesus told them, 'Let the children come to me. Don't block the way. Don't close up the passage. Children belong to God's family.' "

Peter hoped his friends understood the story as well as he did. Another day he would tell it to them again. And another day they might say more of the missing words that Mother and Father still needed. He would listen for them.

New Words in the Story

adiós	ah-dee-OHS	Nta li	ntah lee
Camilla	kah-MEE-yah	Raimundo	rye-MOON-doh
Emilio	ay-MEE-lee-oh	Si sca	see skah
Esteban	es-TAY-bahn	tortilla	tor-TEE-yah
Mazateco	mah-zah-TAY-koh		

9
Jaime's Big Question

Jaime always seemed to be asking questions. He asked them any time of day or night. He asked them at any place. There always seemed to be something that Jaime wanted to know! Mama and Papa often wondered how seven-year-old Jaime could be so curious about everything in and around their village home in Brazil.

Jaime asked Mama, "Why does smoke go up?"

"Where do the clouds go when they disappear?"

"How does the sweet water get inside the orange?"

Mama, busy with cooking, cleaning, and sewing in the small house, had to stop her work. "Jaime," she said, "how do you think of so many questions?

Go find Luís and play with him. Go watch your animal friends in the woods."

To Mama it seemed that Jaime wondered about everything.

Jaime asked Papa, "Why is the sky blue?"

"Why is the sun yellow? And grass green?"

"Where does the rain hide before it comes down?"

Papa, busy in the yard mixing mud and straw to make adobe bricks for walls of new village houses, had to stop his work. "Jaime," he said, trying not to sound impatient, "come and help me put the bricks in straight rows to dry. Busy boys have little time for questions."

To Papa it seemed there was never a day without a question from Jaime. And there wasn't! There was so much that Jaime wanted to know.

One day while Jaime helped Papa put the drying bricks in long, neat rows, he forgot that busy boys had little time for questions.

"Papa, whose house will have these bricks?"

"Where will he build the house?"

"When will he build it?"

Papa threw up his hands. "I should have told you. These bricks are for a schoolhouse, not a house to live in. Villagers will build it. When it is ready, a teacher will come from the misson school. All that he knows and all that he reads from his books he will share with you and the other village children. Ask him your questions!" Today Papa seemed not to mind Jaime's curiosity.

A school! A teacher! Jaime had never been to a school nor had he seen one. But he knew what a school was for. He knew that he would like going to it, if the teacher could answer his questions and help him learn all he wanted to know.

In the days that followed, Jaime gladly helped Papa make bricks. Other villagers carried them away and began to build the school. Others built doors, tables, benches, and shelves to put in the school. Mama and the village women sewed bright cloth for curtains. Children planted seeds that in time would become bright flowers along the path.

When everyone looked at the finished work, they were pleased. They exclaimed in their Portuguese words. "*Que beleza!* Beautiful! It is indeed beautiful!"

On the first morning of school, when Jaime and the other children heard the bell, they hurried to their lessons. They listened as the teacher introduced himself. "I am your friend, Senhor Tomás." Then they told their names.

When Jaime could wait no longer, he went up to the teacher and stood beside him. Out came his questions.

"Where did you come from?"

"Do you know about everything?"

"What will we do at this school?"

Senhor Tomás answered Jaime's questions so that all the children could hear. "I came from the mission school in the city of Rio de Janeiro. Teachers there helped me to become a teacher. No, I don't know about everything, but what I know I'll gladly share with all of you. We'll learn our numbers. We'll learn to read and write our Portuguese words. We'll learn about our country of Brazil and about people in other lands whose language is different from ours.

We'll listen to stories from my favorite book, the Bible."

Jaime was satisfied. School would be good.

And in the days ahead, each school day seemed to Jaime like no other day he had ever known. Each one brought new ideas to think about, new lessons to learn.

Every morning Jaime rolled out of bed and splashed his face with cool water to hurry him awake. He put on his school clothes and often was waiting to eat his breakfast of rolls, coffee, and bananas even before Mama had prepared it. He must be early at school and ready to learn.

Now Jaime had little time for games with Luís. He seldom went any more to the woods to watch his animal friends—the black-eyed monkeys, the bright-feathered chattering parrots, the gentle deer.

One day after many days of school, Jaime had more questions to ask Senhor Tomás.

"Is Rio far away?"

"What is Rio like?"

"How did you come here from there?"

In that day's lesson Senhor Tomás answered the questions. "Rio is almost a day's journey from this village. It is a big city. One side of the city is edged by wide beaches with foamy white waves that dash in from the ocean and splash against the shore. On the other side mountains lift themselves into the sky. The streets are wide, and there are large buildings. Many people live in Rio. My friend, Senhor Elias, lives there. He works in an important building. Some day I'll tell you about him and his work. To come from Rio I traveled on a train-with-a-whistle and on a bus-with-a-horn."

This lesson, like each one that Senhor Tomás taught, was about real places and real people. It was interesting. It was not hard to remember. Jaime wished he could go to Rio and see everything for himself. He would like to travel on a train and a bus.

As the weeks and months passed, Jaime learned to read and print Portuguese words. Once he copied the letters that were on the cover of Senhor Tomás' favorite book—BIBLIA SAGRADA, Holy Bible. He learned to count to one thousand, one hundred, and ninety, the number of pages in this big book. Senhor Tomás said that the Bible was the most important book he knew. Every day he read from it to the children. Jaime liked Bible stories. Often he told them to Mama and Papa. They liked them, too.

One day when Senhor Tomás finished one of the Bible stories, Jaime asked, "Why is the Bible important?"

"Does every person in the world know about it?"

"Could I have one?"

Senhor Tomás seemed glad to talk about his book. "It's important because it tells about God's love for every person born in the world. And because it tells about Jesus, whose life helps people to understand God's love. Some day, perhaps, every person in the world will know about the Bible and be able to read it and study it for himself. Some day I hope each of you will have a Bible of his own."

Jaime thought he understood what Senhor Tomás said, and yet one part puzzled him. He repeated the puzzling part over to himself. "Some day . . . every person in the world will . . . be able to read it and study it for himself." Yet how could this be?

Jaime spoke out to ask more about it. "How can people in all the countries read the Bible when all its words are Portuguese words?"

Senhor Tomás spoke to the class. "Jaime has asked a big question. Who wants to try to answer it?" He repeated the question.

One boy had an idea. "Everybody in all the countries everywhere could learn to read Portuguese."

The others did not agree. "But who would teach them? It would take a long time."

There was another idea. "We could go from Brazil to all the countries of the world and read the Portuguese words to the people."

Again there were objections. "But they wouldn't understand us. We couldn't understand them."

Senhor Tomás said, "The answer to Jaime's big question is this: Bibles are printed in more than one language. Not every Bible has Portuguese words. The Bible was written long, long ago. Some of it was in Hebrew, some in Greek. Now it has been translated into Spanish, French, English, and a thousand more languages. When it is translated into every language and when every person has learned to read, then everyone may know about the Bible."

That night Jaime told Papa and Mama all he had learned that day. The answer to his big question was hard for them to understand, too.

Several days later Senhor Tomás came home with Jaime after school. He showed a letter to Mama and Papa. "I wrote to my friend in Rio and told him about Jaime's big question. In this letter Senhor Elias invites me to bring Jaime to Rio next week during the school holiday. Jaime can see for himself how the Bible is printed in the Portuguese language. My friend will show him. May he go?"

So it was that one morning the next week when the bus-with-a-horn clattered to its stop in the village, Jaime and Senhor Tomás were waiting for it. Jaime, wearing his seldom worn shoes and socks, followed Senhor Tomás inside the bus. *"Até logo!"* He waved through the window to Mama and Papa and his friends from school.

"Good-by!" they called back as the bus clattered away toward Rio.

After a little while, Jaime and Senhor Tomás left the bus and climbed aboard a train-with-a-whistle. Before night they were in the mission school in Rio, their home for the days of the visit. This night Jaime was too tired even to ask questions, but the next morning he began.

"Is it far to the important building?"

"When do we start?"

"Will I soon see your friend?"

Senhor Tomás said, "Today I think you will find
these answers for yourself."

At the end of rides on a rocking, rolling streetcar
and a bouncing, bumping bus Jaime saw in front of
him a long, low building that seemed to stretch
out as far as he could see. And coming through the
door was a man.

"It's Senhor Elias himself!" cried Senhor Tomás.

"This is our Bible printing house," Senhor Elias
said, after greeting them. "Come, I want to show you
everything."

All that day, from one end of the printing house to the other, Jaime and Senhor Tomás followed, watched, and listened.

"Here's the paper—stacks and stacks of it—brought to us in a ship from across the ocean."

"This sharp-edged knife cuts the paper to make the Bibles' pages the right size."

"Each of these trays holds metal letters in place ready to be inked to print one page."

"This big roller spreads ink on the metal letters, and this one rolls the paper against the inked letters."

"This machine folds the printed pages. This one sews the pages together. This one cuts the edges even. This one sews on the covers."

"And here are the finished copies!"

Seeing, hearing, and learning so much, Jaime could only stare at the hundreds of books stamped with the familiar words BIBLIA SAGRADA, Holy Bible. For once, he could think of not even one question!

Senhor Elias continued, "Presses in other countries print Bibles in other languages—in more than a thousand languages. Each year around the world

Bibles or portions of Bibles are printed in new languages that have never been printed before."

When the visit was over and the guests were at the door, Senhor Elias gave a package to each of them. He told Senhor Tomás, "Your box contains copies of Bible stories for children. Please give one to each pupil in your school."

From Jaime's box he lifted a Bible, one like those that Jaime had seen coming from the binding machine. The words BIBLIA SAGRADA were stamped in gold across the top and below them, in smaller gold letters, was another word—JAIME.

"This is for you," Senhor Elias said, "to read and to keep for all the days of your life."

Jaime could only answer, "Oh, sir, thank you. I will read it every day."

NEW WORDS IN THE STORY

até logo	ah-TAY LAH-goh	Senhor	sehn-YOR
Elias	eh-LEE-ahs	Tomás	toh-MAHS
Jaime	ZHYE-mee	Luís	loo-EEZ
Biblia Sagrada	BEE-blee-ah sah-GRAH-dah		
Que beleza	keh beh-LAY-zah		

10

The Yesu Book

Ntange seemed little different from the other seven-year-old boys in his Congo village. He had a house to live in—a one-room house with dried mud walls and a roof of grass. He had clothes to wear—shorts and a bright shirt. He had food to eat—porridge, mashed peanuts, and greens from the garden. He had toys to play with—a bow and arrow and a rolling hoop made from forest vines. He had work to do—helping Mother and Father at home and in the fields.

Ntange never thought of wanting anything more than he already had.

Then one day something new happened. It began

when he heard the drum call sounding through the village.

> Come, my children!
>> Come! See!
> Put your bows and arrows down.
> Put your rolling hoops away.
> Hurry on the winding path.
> Hurry to the shady place.
> The Yesu book is here.
>> Come! See!

"What is this Yesu book?" Ntange asked Mother. Mother did not know. She had never seen such a book.

"What is this Yesu book?" Ntange asked Father.

Father said, "I think it is the book of the Christian teacher. She has come to help the villagers plan for our church. The drummer sends the message for her. Do as the message says. Go and see for yourself."

Ntange put down his toys and hurried along the path. Koli, Malia, and other children also were on the path. When at last they came to the shady place,

Ntange saw that Father was right. The new Christian teacher was there waiting for them.

The teacher said, "I have come to live for a while in your village. I have brought something to share with you."

She held up a few books, and the children counted them—one, two, three, four.

"Each is a Yesu book. They are all alike," she said. "They tell the stories of Yesu in your language."

The teacher opened one of the books, and the children crowded closer to see the bright pictures. Ntange reached out with his hand and touched the pictured green hillside with its many-colored flowers. He had never seen a place like this, so different from his forest village.

"Yesu lived in a land far away from here," the teacher said. She then turned to another picture. "This is Yesu. He lived long ago. He was a teacher. He was a friend."

Ntange looked closely at the pictured man. He wore strange clothing, not like Father's, not like that of the teacher at school, not like that of any man in the whole village. Yet if Yesu were a teacher and a friend, Ntange understood about him. Teachers helped people to learn. Friends made you glad to be with them.

The teacher showed other pages. Ntange and the other children looked at each bright picture in its turn. One after another they asked, "What is this—and this—and this?"

And with the answers, the teacher told a story about what each child had seen.

Finally the teacher closed the book. "No more to-day. Come in two days to my house across the clearing. Then we will look at the book again."

Ntange picked up one of the books beside the teacher. "I want this Yesu book," he said.

Koli put out his hand for a book. "I want one."

Malia picked up another. "So do I," she said.

"I cannot give you a book," the teacher explained. "You can buy one for three pennies. Boys and girls of North America sent the books with the pictures to us, but we had to print the stories in your language, and that costs money."

Three pennies! It seemed a lot of money to Ntange.

He gave the book back to the teacher and reached his hand toward his pocket. But there was no use putting it inside. He knew he had no coins.

That night Ntange told Mother, "I need three pennies. I want to buy a Yesu book. The teacher has four books to sell."

Mother said, "You have your bow and arrow, your rolling hoop. Be content with those."

That night, lying on his mat before he fell asleep, Ntange thought again about the bright pictures of Yesu, the teacher, the friend. He thought of all the stories that told about Yesu. "If I had such a book, I'd look at it every morning. I'd look at it every night. I'd keep it beside my sleeping mat, safe from rain and sun."

The next day when Ntange walked beside Father to the fields beyond the village, he told Father, "I need three pennies. I want a Yesu book."

Father said, "There are books at school. Why can't you use those instead?"

Ntange explained, "Schoolbooks have no bright

pictures. Schoolbooks must remain at school. I want a book for myself at home."

Father said, "This is not the time to talk of books. Use your hoe now and help me clear the field for planting."

The next morning, Ntange hurried to the Christian teacher's house. It was the day to see the pictures again, to hear another story. But as Ntange followed the other children into the teacher's house, he saw that Koli was already there! Koli was counting aloud, "One, two, three." Koli was placing coins in a row on the teacher's table.

Ntange watched while the teacher took a Yesu book from the shelf and gave it to Koli. Koli did not stay for stories with the teacher. He hurried toward home. Ntange thought, "If I had a book I would hurry home, too, and look at every page."

Later when Ntange passed Koli's house, he heard his friend spelling out the words and reading the stories to his small brother.

"I could spell. I could read," he thought, "if only I had the Yesu book."

At home Ntange told Mother, "Koli bought a book. Now there are three left."

Mother said, "You are a help to me in the fields. I wish I could pay you for frightening the birds away from our grain. But our coins are needed to buy salt, flour, and other food for our family."

Ntange told Father, "Koli bought a Yesu book. I want pennies to buy one."

Father said, "You are a help to me in the forest. I wish I could pay you for hunting and finding the stumps I need to make stools and tables for village houses. But our coins are needed to buy cloth, needles, and thread for Mother to sew our clothing."

On another day when Ntange hurried to the teacher's house to see the Yesu book again, Malia came, too. She untied the corner of her blue head-cloth and took out three coins. She gave them to the teacher. Ntange watched while the teacher took a Yesu book from the shelf and handed it to Malia. Malia wrapped the book carefully in her headcloth. "I go. You stay." She called her good-by and hurried away.

At home Ntange told Mother, "Only two books are now on the shelf in the teacher's house."

The next day Ntange went down by the river. Village women had been fishing. Now they were bringing in their catch. "They need help," thought Ntange. "They will have three pennies for me."

He went to one of the women. "I'll take the fish from your nets."

The woman answered, "No, oh no! Old Mister Crocodile suns himself here on the sand. He likes small boys for his supper. His long strong tail might flap you into the water. Then we'd never see you again."

Walking toward home, Ntange heard a neighbor pounding damp clay to make a new floor in her house. He hurried there. "I'll help you pound. If you pay me three pennies, I can buy a Yesu book."

The woman continued to beat the palm-branch bat against the clay to make it firm and glazed like brick. "No, oh no! A small boy is not strong enough for the pounding," she answered.

Ntange passed another house and saw a neighbor

climb to the top of his house and begin to tie on the roofing grass, making it thick and even. "I could help," he called.

"No, oh no!" the man replied. "I could not let you help me tie the roofing grass on my house. A fall from up here where I am would break your bones."

Then Ntange passed another neighbor's house. This woman was not working. She was sitting quietly in her doorway. But in her hand was a Yesu book! She was looking at the bright pictures. Now she began to read aloud some of the words.

"Now only one book stands on the shelf," Ntange told Mother. "Soon someone will take coins and buy it. Then there will be no book. Tomorrow I will go early to the teacher's house. I will see if the book is still there."

But early the next day Father told Ntange, "Come with me to the forest. I need you." And when Ntange finished there, Mother said, "Go and bring water for me from the river. I need your help." When he finished, it was late afternoon. Ntange hurried to the teacher's house.

Through the open door he saw the teacher busy at the table. He looked beyond her to the shelf. The Yesu book was there! No one had come to buy it. He would wait until the teacher finished her work, then he would ask to hold it again, to see the bright pictures.

But the teacher looked up. "Come in, Ntange," she invited. "It is late now, but I am especially glad to see you. This morning Itofe cut the weeds in my yard, but he had to leave before he gathered them up to throw away. Look! If they dry on the ground they will send their seeds back into the earth. Will you gather them for me?"

Ntange was tired, but he went to the yard and began the work. Soon he returned to the door. "Your weeds are in the big can. You can burn them now."

The teacher was surprised to have the work finished so quickly. "You have worked well. I am pleased. Now—here is something for you." Turning back to the shelf, she took the Yesu book, the last one, from its place and gave it to Ntange. "It is yours. You have earned it. Enjoy the pictures every day.

One day you will know all the words and read them. Then you can share them with others."

Ntange liked her words. Yes, some day he would be the teacher. Now he must hurry home. He must show Father and Mother the Yesu book and tell them how he had earned it for himself.

NEW WORDS IN THE STORY

Itofe	ee-TOH-feh	Malia	mah-LEE-ah
Koli	KOH-lee	Ntange	n-TAH-ngeh
Yesu	YEH-SOO		

TEXT: *14 point Caledonia leaded 6 points*
COMPOSITION, PRINTING, AND BINDING:
Sowers Printing Company
COVERS AND JACKETS: *Affiliated Lithographers, Inc.*
TYPOGRAPHICAL DESIGN: *Barbara M. Knox*
BINDING DESIGN: *Louise E. Jefferson*